WORLD'S BIBLE STORY LIBRARY

VOLUME 1

Creation to Isaac's Blessing

BY

J. HAROLD GWYNNE, D.D.

ILLUSTRATED BY

STEELE SAVAGE

The World Publishing Company

New York

WORLD'S BIBLE STORY LIBRARY

is published by The World Publishing Company

WORLD PUBLISHING
TIMES MIRROR

Contents

II. Stories About Moses and the Israelites   47

VOLUME 3

III. Stories About Joshua and the Judges   29

VOLUME 4

IV. Stories About Three Kings of United Israel

VOLUME 5

VOLUME 6

From the New Testament

VOLUME 7

VOLUME 8

II. The Book of Acts   23

FROM THE OLD TESTAMENT

I.

STORIES

OF THE

HEBREW

PATRIARCHS

God's Work of Creation

Genesis 1:1–2:9

IN THE beginning God created the heaven and the earth. That was a long, long time ago. How long ago, people do not agree. Many say we can never really know. But it is known that God existed before the world was made, and that He created all things by His wisdom and power.

the act of making something

At the very beginning, the earth was far different from the way it looks now. It was a formless mass; empty and blank and utterly void of life. Deep waters covered the surface of the earth, and complete darkness was everywhere. But the Spirit of God moved upon the face of the waters to bring order and beauty out of dark and fearful chaos.

God's work of creation extended, as we are told, over six days, to give us the familiar things of our world—day and night, the sky overhead, the oceans, and the dry land. Then came the fishes and the birds, the land animals, the people. Our world would be a strange place indeed if any one of the days of creation had been left out.

At first God said, "Let there be light." And light was created. God saw that it was good; and He divided the light from the darkness. And God called the light Day, and the darkness He called Night. And the evening and the morning were the first day of creation.

sky Next God said, "Let there be a <u>firmament</u> in the midst of the waters, to divide the waters above and below." So God made the beautiful sky, and created the clouds to carry the sky moisture above the water-covered earth below. And God called the firmament Heaven. This was God's work of creation on the second day.

On the third day, God caused the waters to gather together in wide, deep places and called them Seas. He also caused dry land to appear, and called it Earth. And God saw that this was good. Then God said, "Let the earth bring forth plants, those producing seed, and fruit trees producing fruit which bears its own seed, each after its kind, upon the earth." And it was so. And God saw that it was good. And the evening and the morning were the third day of creation.

The fourth day God said, "Let there be lights in the firmament of the heaven to divide the day from the night; and let them be for signs and for seasons and for days and years, and let them be for lights in the heaven to give light upon the earth." And this came to pass. And God made two great lights, the sun to rule the day and the moon to rule the night; He made the stars also. And God saw that it was good. Thus ended the fourth day of creation.

On the fifth day God said, "Let the waters bring forth great numbers of moving creatures, and birds that may fly above the earth in the open firmament of heaven." So God created great whales and every living creature that swims in the waters, after its kind; and every flying bird after its kind. And God saw that it was good. And God blessed them, saying, "Be fruitful, and multiply, and fill the waters in the seas, and let birds multiply in the earth." And the evening and the morning were the fifth day of creation.

On the sixth day God said, "Let the earth bring forth living creatures after their kinds: cattle, and creeping things, and beasts of the earth." And it was so. And God saw that it was good.

But God's highest creative work was yet to come. For God said, "Let us make man in our image, after our likeness; and let him have dominion over the fish of the sea, and over the birds of the air, and over the cattle, and over all the earth, and over every creeping thing that creeps upon the earth." So God created man in his own image; male and female He created them. And God blessed them and said, "Be fruitful and multiply, and replenish the earth and subdue it; and have dominion over

animals

make a new supply

the fish of the sea, and over the birds of the air, and over every living thing that moves upon the earth."

And God said to man, "Behold, I have given you every plant producing seed which is upon the face of the earth, and every tree producing fruit which bears its own seed; they shall be yours for food. And to every beast of the earth, and to every bird of the air, and to everything that creeps upon the earth, everything in which there is life, I have given all green plants for food." And it was so. And God saw everything that He had made, and behold, it was very good. And this completed the sixth day of creation.

Thus the heaven and the earth were finished, and all the host of them. And God rested on the seventh day from all the work which He had done. And God blessed the seventh day, and <u>sanctified</u> it, because on it He rested from all the work of creation which He had done.

set apart for religious use

The Lord God had formed man of the dust of the ground, and had breathed into his nostrils the breath of life; so that man became a living being. Then the Lord God planted a garden to the east in Eden; and there the Lord God put the man whom He had created. And out of the ground in the garden of Eden the Lord God made grow every tree that is pleasant to the sight and good for food. There was also the tree of life growing in the

midst of the garden, and the tree of knowledge of good and evil. Thus, in this happy
paradise, the first man and the first woman
dwelt in fellowship and communion with the
God who had created them.

heavenlike place

The Transgression
of Adam and Eve

Genesis 2:10–3:24

A RIVER flowed out of Eden to water the garden, and from there it divided into four branches. The first was named Pison, and it flowed around the whole land of Havilah, where there was much fine gold and bdellium and onyx stone. The name of the second river was Gihon, and it flowed around the whole land of Ethiopia. The third river, named Hiddekel, flowed to the east of Assyria. And the fourth river was the great river Euphrates.

a dark red gem

The Lord God took the man and put him in the garden of Eden to cultivate it and keep it. And the Lord God commanded the man, saying, "You are free to eat of every tree of the garden; but you shall not eat of the tree of the knowledge of good and evil, for in the day that you eat of it you shall die."

Then the Lord God said, "It is not good that the man should be alone; I will make him a helpmeet to be a companion for him."

a good helper

In the meantime the Lord God formed out of the ground every beast of the field and

18

every bird of the air, and brought them to Adam to see what he would call them; and whatever Adam called each living creature, that was its name. So Adam gave names to all cattle, and to the birds of the air, and to every beast of the field. But for Adam there was not found a suitable mate.

So the Lord God caused a deep sleep to fall upon Adam, and while he slept took one of his ribs and closed up the empty space with flesh. And from the rib which the Lord God had taken from man He made a woman and brought her to the man.

And Adam said, "This is now bone of my bones and flesh of my flesh; she shall be called Woman, because she was taken out of Man." Therefore, according to God's plan, a man shall leave his father and mother and cleave to his wife, and they shall be as one flesh. And both man and woman were naked, but in their state of purity and innocence they were not ashamed.

hold near or stay with

But, alas, the man and the woman did not long remain in this state of purity and innocence. They were soon to disobey God's commandment and commit evil. This is the way it came about.

The serpent was more crafty than any beast of the field which the Lord God had made. One day in the garden the serpent said to the woman, "Has not God indeed said, 'You shall not eat of every tree of the garden'?" And the

tricky

woman said to the serpent, "We are permitted to eat of the fruit of the trees of the garden; but of the tree which is in the <u>midst</u> of the garden God said, 'You are not to eat of its fruit nor to touch it; if you do, you will die.' "

But the serpent, telling a lie, said to the woman, "You will not really die. For God knows that whenever you eat of it your eyes will be opened and you will be as gods, knowing good and evil."

So the woman was deceived and <u>yielded</u> to temptation. When she saw that the tree was good for food, and that it was pleasant to the eyes, and a tree to be desired to make one wise, she took some of its fruit and ate; and also gave some to her husband, and he ate. And the eyes of them both were opened, and they knew that they were naked, and for the first time they felt ashamed. To cover their nakedness they sewed fig leaves together and made themselves aprons.

Then, to their dismay, they heard the voice of the Lord God in the garden in the cool of the day, and Adam and his wife hid themselves from the presence of the Lord God among the trees of the garden. But the Lord God called to Adam, and said to him, "Where are you?" And Adam said, "I heard your voice in the garden and I was afraid, because I was naked; and I hid myself."

The Lord God said to Adam, "Who told you that you were naked? Have you eaten the

middle

gave in

fruit of the tree of which I commanded you, 'You shall not eat of it'?" Adam, seeking to excuse himself from blame, replied, "The woman whom you gave to be with me gave me some of the fruit of the tree, and I ate." Then the Lord God said to the woman, "What is this wicked thing that you have done?" The woman, seeking to excuse her-

cheated or tricked

self, said, "The serpent beguiled and tempted me, and I ate."

Then the Lord God said to the serpent, "Because you have done this, you are cursed above all cattle, and above every beast of the field; you shall crawl upon your belly, and you shall eat dust all the days of your life. I will cause enmity between you and the woman, and between your progeny and her progeny. The progeny of the woman shall bruise your head, and you shall bruise their heel."

To the woman God said, "I will greatly

great pain

multiply your travail in childbearing; in pain and suffering shall you bring forth children; also your desire shall be for your husband, and he shall rule over you."

And to Adam the Lord said, "Because you have heeded the voice of your wife, and have eaten of the tree of which I commanded you, 'You shall not eat of it,' cursed is the ground on your account; in labor and sorrow you shall eat of it all the days of your life; thorns and thistles it shall bring forth to trouble you;

and you shall eat the plants of the field. In the sweat of your face you shall eat bread till you return to the ground, for out of it you were taken; you are made from the dust, and to dust you shall return."

Adam called his wife's name Eve, because she was the mother of all living. And for Adam and Eve the Lord God made garments of skins, and clothed them.

And the Lord God said, "Behold, the man has become as one of us, in that he knows good and evil; and now, in order that he may not put forth his hand and take also of the tree of life, and eat, and live forever, I will send him forth from the garden of Eden, to till the ground from which he was taken."

So the Lord God drove the man out from his garden of paradise. And at the east of the garden of Eden the Lord placed <u>Cherubim</u>, angels and a flaming sword which turned in all directions, to guard the way of the tree of life.

Cain Slays His Brother Abel

Genesis 4:1–26

THE first son born to Adam and Eve, after they were <u>expelled</u> from the garden of Eden, was named Cain. At the time of his birth, Eve, the first mother, said, "I have given birth to a son, due to the presence of the Lord." Some time later Eve gave birth to a second son whom she called Abel.

sent away as punishment

The years passed, and the brothers Cain and Abel grew up and became young men. Abel became a shepherd and took care of flocks of sheep. Cain became a tiller of the ground and raised different crops that grow in the earth.

In time Cain brought the Lord an offering of the fruit of the ground which he had harvested. At the same time Abel brought the Lord an offering of the <u>firstlings</u> of his flock of sheep and of their fat. And the Lord accepted and received Abel and his offering, but Cain and his offering were not acceptable to the Lord. There was something about Cain's life and spirit which the Lord did not approve.

first born

The Lord God drove them out from his garden of paradise

the look on a
person's face

Cain became very angry when his offering was not accepted, and his <u>countenance</u> became dark and sullen. The Lord said to Cain, "Why are you angry, and why has your countenance darkened? If you do well, will you not be accepted? And if you do not do well, sin lies at the door; it desires you, but you shall rule over it."

think in a
worried way

But Cain did not heed the word of the Lord. He continued to <u>brood</u> in anger and envy against his brother Abel. And one day, when Cain and Abel were in the field, Cain suddenly rose up against his brother, struck him with a heavy club, and killed him.

And the Lord said to Cain, the first murderer, "Where is Abel your brother?" The guilty man replied, "I do not know; am I my brother's keeper?" And the Lord said, "What have you done? The voice of your brother's blood cries to me from the ground. And now you are cursed from the earth, which has opened her mouth to receive your brother's blood from your hand. When you till the ground it shall no longer yield to you its strength; you shall be a fugitive and a vagabond in the earth."

Then the remorseful Cain said to the Lord, "My punishment is greater than I can bear. Behold, you have driven me out today from the face of the earth; and from your face I shall be hidden; and I shall be a fugitive and a vagabond in the earth, and everyone who finds me will want to slay me."

But the Lord said to him, "This shall not be. Whoever slays Cain shall be <u>revenged</u> sevenfold." And the Lord set a mark on Cain, lest any who encountered him should kill him. Then Cain left the presence of the Lord, and dwelt in the land of Nod, which means "wandering," to the east of Eden.

After the death of her second son Abel, Eve gave birth to a third son whom she called Seth. "For God," Eve said, "has given me another son instead of Abel, whom Cain slew." In due time, to Seth also was born a son, whom he called Enos. From that time men began to call upon the name of the Lord in prayer and worship. Thus Seth became the father of the godly line of descendants of whom Noah was born.

revenged
paid back for
evil done

Noah Builds the Ark

Genesis 6:1–8:22

WHEN men began to multiply on the earth, and daughters were born to them, the young men saw that these daughters were fair; and they chose them to become their wives.

become more, increase

As time went on, the world became filled with evil. And God saw that the wickedness of man was great in the earth, and that the imagination of man's heart was only continuously evil. And the Lord regretted that he had made man on the earth, and it grieved his heart. And the Lord said, "I will destroy man, whom I have created, from the face of the earth, man and beast and creeping things and birds of the air, for I regret that I have made them."

One of the descendants of Seth, after many generations had passed, was Noah, the son of Lamech. Noah was a just man, and guiltless in his generation because he walked with God. He had three sons, Shem, Ham, and Japheth. And Noah found favor in the eyes of

Cain slew his brother Abel

believed to be wood
from pine or fir tree

the Lord. God said to Noah, "I am going to destroy all living creatures, for the earth is filled with violence through them; behold, I will destroy them with the earth. Therefore build an ark of gopher wood; make rooms in the ark, and seal it inside and out with pitch."

Then the Lord instructed Noah to make the ark four hundred and fifty feet long, seventy-five feet wide, and forty-five feet high. A window was to be built for the ark; a door was to be set in one side; and the ark was to have lower, second, and third stories.

The Lord told Noah, "Behold, I will bring a flood of waters upon the earth, to destroy all flesh, in which is the breath of life, from under heaven; everything that is in the earth shall die. But with you I will establish my covenant; and you shall come into the ark, you, and your sons, and your wife, and your sons' wives with you."

make

The Lord commanded Noah further, saying, "Of every living thing of all flesh, you shall bring two of every sort, male and female, into the ark, to keep them alive with you. Of birds after their kind, and of cattle after their kind, of every creeping thing of the earth after its kind, two of every sort shall come to you to keep them alive. And take with you all food that is eaten, and store it away, and it shall be food for you and for them." Thus Noah did all that God commanded him to do.

Then the Lord commanded Noah to enter

into the ark with all the members of his family, eight persons in all. And Noah and his wife and his three sons and their wives went into the ark, to escape the flood which was to be upon the earth. And according to God's law commandment, Noah took with him into the ark seven pairs of all clean animals, male and female; a pair of unclean animals, male and female; and seven pairs of the birds of the air, male and female. These all went two by two with Noah into the ark.

And after seven days the waters of the flood came upon the earth. On the seventeenth day of the second month all the fountains of the great deep burst forth, and the windows of swift and heavy flows heaven were opened. And torrents of rain fell upon the earth for forty days and forty nights. But Noah and his family were safely sheltered and protected in the ark.

As the flood continued upon the earth, the waters increased and bore up the ark; and it was lifted up above the earth, where it floated on the face of the waters. And the waters prevailed greatly upon the earth; and all the high mountains were covered over with many feet of water.

And all flesh died that moved upon the earth, birds, cattle, beasts, and every creeping thing that crept upon the earth, and every man; every living thing on the earth perished in the flood of waters. Only Noah and those that were with him in the ark were alive and safe. And the flood lasted for a hundred and fifty days.

But God remembered Noah and all the living creatures that were with him in the ark. And God made a wind blow over the earth, and the waters subsided; the fountains of the deep and the windows of heaven were stopped, and the rain from heaven was restrained, and the waters receded from the earth continually. And after a hundred and fifty days the waters were abated; and the ark came to rest, in the seventh month, on the seventeenth day of the month, upon the mountains of Ararat. And the waters decreased continually until the tenth month; on the first day of that month the tops of the mountains were visible.

went down

At the end of forty days Noah opened the window of the ark which he had made, and sent forth a raven, which went to and fro until the waters were dried up from the earth. He also sent forth a dove, to see if the waters had abated from the face of the earth. But the dove found no place to rest her foot, and returned to the ark, for the waters were still upon the face of the whole earth. Then Noah stretched forth his hand and pulled the dove back into the ark with him.

Noah waited another seven days, and again sent forth the dove from the ark. And the dove returned in the evening, and lo, in her mouth she had a newly plucked olive leaf. So Noah knew that the waters had abated from

33

the earth. He waited then yet another seven days, and sent forth the dove a third time; this time it did not return again.

In the first day of the first month of the new year, the waters were dried from off the earth; and Noah removed the covering of the ark and looked out, and behold, the ground was dry. On the twenty-seventh day of the second month, the earth was completely dry.

Then God spoke to Noah, saying, "Go forth from the ark, you, and your wife, and your sons, and your sons' wives with you. Bring forth with you every living thing that is with you, of all flesh—the birds, the beasts, and every creeping thing that creeps upon the earth—so that they may breed abundantly upon the earth, and be fruitful and multiply upon the earth." So Noah went forth, and the members of his family with him. Every beast, every creeping thing, and every bird, everything that creeps upon the earth, after its kind, went forth out of the ark.

And in that fresh, clean, new world, Noah built an altar to the Lord, and took of every clean beast and of every clean bird, and offered burnt offerings on the altar. And the

a special taste
or smell

Lord smelled the sweet <u>savor</u> of Noah's offering, and said in his heart, "I will never again curse the ground on man's account, even though the imagination of man's heart is evil from his youth; neither will I ever again destroy all living things, as I have done. While

And in the dove's mouth was a newly plucked olive leaf

the earth remains, seed time and harvest, cold and heat, summer and winter, and day and night shall not <u>cease</u>."

stop

And God established a covenant with Noah and his descendants that He would never again destroy all flesh upon the earth by the waters of a great flood. And as a token of this everlasting covenant, God set a beautiful rainbow in the clouds of the sky.

The Tower of Babel

Genesis 10:1–11:9

AFTER the flood, the three sons of Noah —Shem, Ham, and Japheth— raised large families of sons and daughters. These families in turn increased and multiplied into tribes and nations, which spread abroad into different lands and developed different languages. Thus the descendants of Shem, Ham, and Japheth formed the various peoples and nations that we read about in later Bible history.

In the early period of new beginnings after the flood, the whole earth had but one language. And it came to pass, as men came from the east, that they found a plain in the land of Shinar, or Babylonia, and settled there. After a time they said to one another, "Come, let us make bricks and bake them thoroughly." And they made great quantities of bricks to use for stone, and learned how they could use mud for <u>mortar</u>.

Then these dwellers in Shinar said, "Let us come together and build ourselves a city, and a tower whose top will reach to heaven, and let us make a name for ourselves, lest we be

mortar: that which holds bricks together

37

scattered abroad upon the face of the whole earth." So all the people began to build. Many brick houses were erected for the people to live in. But the greatest undertaking was the huge tower which rose to a great height above the plain of Shinar. The people thought this tower would be a great and lasting monument to their industry and <u>ingenuity</u>.

skill and cleverness

But their selfish pride in this vast undertaking displeased the God of heaven. And the Lord came down to see the city and the tower which the children of men had built.

And the Lord said, "Behold, they are all one people and they all speak one language; and this is only the beginning of what they intend to do; now nothing which they imagine will be impossible for them to carry out. Come, we will go down, and there confound their language, so that they may not be able to understand one another's speech."

So the Lord of heaven and earth con<u>founded</u> their language by causing them to speak with different tongues, so that they could not understand one another. And the Lord scattered them abroad from the plain of Shinar over the face of all the earth, and they left off building the city. And the tall tower remained unfinished.

mixed up or confused

Therefore the name of the tower was called Babel, which means "the place of God's judgment," because there the Lord confounded the language of all the earth; and from there the Lord scattered the people of Babylonia into other regions of the earth.

39

A tower whose top will reach to heaven

God's Call

and Promise to Abraham

Genesis 11:27–12:20

THE life story of Abraham is one of the most important of all the Old Testament stories, for it marks the beginning of a new era in human history and in God's plan of redemption. Abraham was the son of Terah, forefather of the Hebrew people, father of the faithful, friend of God.

Terah lived in the city of Ur in the land of Chaldea. He had three sons, Abraham, Nahor, and Haran. Terah was seventy years old when Abraham was born. Haran, who was the father of Lot, died in the land of his birth before his father Terah. Abraham married a wife by the name of Sarai, and Nahor married a woman by the name of Milcah.

worship of idols by
uncivilized people

Desiring to get away from the evil influence of <u>heathen idolatry</u> in Ur of Chaldea, Terah took his family and went forth to go into the land of Canaan. In the family group were Terah, Abraham and Sarai, and Lot, Terah's grandson, the son of Haran. They journeyed northward through the valley of the Euphrates River until they came to the land of Haran, where they settled for a time. Some time later Terah died in Haran; he did not live to reach the land of Canaan.

While Abraham continued to sojourn in Haran, the Lord God spoke to him and said, "Go forth from your own country and your own kindred and your father's house to the land that I will show you. And I will make of your descendants a great nation, and I will bless you, and make your name great, and you will be a blessing. I will bless those who bless you, and curse anyone who curses you; and through you all the families of the earth will be blessed."

So by faith Abraham set forth as the Lord had told him; and Lot went with him. Abraham was seventy-five years old when he departed from Haran. And Abraham took with him Sarai his wife, and Lot his brother's son, and all the persons and possessions which they had gathered in Haran; and they went forth on the long journey to the land of Canaan. Their long trek led them across mountains, deserts, and rivers over the westward route that led through Damascus, and southward to Canaan. After perhaps a year of toilsome travel and many adventures, they finally came to the land of Canaan. And Abraham and his family passed through the land until they came to the place called Sichem, to the plain of Moreh. At that time the Canaanites

relatives or family

a slow journey

41

were still in the land.

There the Lord appeared to Abraham and said, "To your posterity I will give this land." So Abraham built an altar there to the Lord, who had appeared to him. From there Abraham removed to a mountain on the east of Bethel, and pitched his tent, with Bethel on the west and Hai on the east. And there also Abraham built an altar to the Lord and called upon the name of the Lord. Soon Abraham journeyed on, still going toward the south.

It came to pass that there was a famine in the land of Canaan, and Abraham went down into Egypt to escape the famine. When they were nearing Egypt, Abraham said to Sarai his wife, "I know that you are a beautiful woman; therefore, when the Egyptians see you, they will say that you are my wife; and they will want to kill me so that they may take you for themselves. Therefore tell them that you are my sister, so that it may go well with me on your account, and my life may be spared because of you."

When Abraham came into Egypt the Egyptians saw that Sarai was indeed very beautiful. The princes of Pharaoh also saw her, and sang her praises to Pharaoh. And Sarai was taken into Pharaoh's house. And for her sake Pharaoh treated Abraham well; and gave him presents of sheep and cattle, and menservants and maidservants to serve him.

But the Lord sent great plagues upon

people of future times, especially in same family

43

Abraham and his family came to the land of Canaan

Pharaoh and his household because of Sarai, Abraham's wife. So Pharaoh called Abraham, and said to him, "Why have you·done this to me? Why did you not tell me that Sarai was your wife? Why did you pretend that she was your sister, so that I could take her for my wife? Now then, here is your wife, take her, and go your way." And Pharaoh issued orders to his men concerning Abraham; and they sent him away, with his wife and family and all his flocks and herds.

And Abraham went up out of the land of Egypt, he and his wife, his nephew Lot, and all that he had, and they came again into the southern country called the Negeb.

God's Covenant
With Abraham

Genesis 15:1–21; 17:15–21; 21:1–8

WHILE Abraham was living near the oaks of Mamre near Hebron, the word of the Lord came to him in a vision, saying, "Fear not, Abraham, I am your shield and your exceedingly great reward." And Abraham said, "Lord God, what will you give me, seeing that I am childless, and that my servant Eliezer of Damascus is the only heir of my house?" And Abraham spoke further to the Lord, saying, "Behold, you have given me no child; and a servant born in my house is my heir."

And behold, the word of the Lord came to Abraham, saying, "The one you speak of shall not be your heir; but your own son shall be your heir." And the Lord brought Abraham out of his tent at night and said, "Look upward to heaven and count the stars, if you are able." Then God said to Abraham, "Your descendants shall likewise be innumerable." And Abraham believed the word of the Lord; and the Lord reckoned it to him as righteousness.

a young cow that
has not yet given
birth to a calf

And God said to Abraham, "I am the Lord who brought you out of Ur in the land of Chaldea, to give you this new land to inherit." Abraham replied, "Lord God, how shall I know that I am to inherit it?" The Lord said to Abraham, "Bring before me now a <u>heifer</u> three years old, a she-goat three years old, a ram three years old, a turtledove, and a young pigeon." Abraham brought all these as directed, cut them in half, and laid each piece one against the other; but the birds he did not cut in half. And when vultures came down upon the carcasses, Abraham drove them away.

As the sun was going down, a deep sleep fell upon Abraham; and lo, a fear of great darkness came upon him. Then the Lord said to Abraham, "Know of a certainty that your descendants will be strangers in a land that is not theirs, and will be servants and slaves there, and will be oppressed and afflicted for four hundred years. But I will bring to judgment the nation which they serve, and in due time they will come forth with great possessions. And you shall be gathered to your fathers in peace; you shall be buried in a good old age. And your descendants shall come here again in the fourth generation; for the iniquity of the Amorites is not yet full and complete."

When the sun had gone down and it was dark, behold, a smoking furnace and a burn-

The word of the Lord came to Abraham

ing lamp passed between the offerings that Abraham had arranged. On that day the Lord made a covenant with Abraham, saying, "To your posterity I will give this land, from the river Nile in Egypt to the great river Euphrates; it is the land now occupied by the Kenites, the Kenizzites, the Kadmonites, the Hittites, the Perizzites, the Rephaims, the Amorites, the Canaanites, the Girgashites, and the Jebusites."

Now Sarai, Abraham's wife, bore him no children. But God said to Abraham, "In regard to Sarai your wife, you shall no longer call her Sarai, but Sarah shall be her name. I will bless her, and also give you a son by her; yes, I will bless her, and she shall be a mother of nations; kings of peoples shall be born of her." Then Abraham fell on his face and laughed, and said to himself, "Shall a child indeed be born to me when I am a hundred years old. And shall Sarah, who is ninety years old, give birth to a child?" But God reaffirmed His promise: "Your wife Sarah shall indeed bear you a son, and you shall call his name Isaac; and I will establish my <u>covenant</u> with him for an everlasting covenant, and with his progeny after him."

important promise
made between
persons, God, groups,
or nations

The Lord visited Sarah as he had said, and the Lord did to Sarah as he had promised. And Sarah bore Abraham a son in his old age at the very time of which God had spoken to him. And Abraham named his son Isaac. And

Abraham <u>circumcised</u> his son Isaac when he was eight days old, as God had commanded him. Abraham was a hundred years old when Isaac was born. And Sarah said, "God has given me laughter; and all who hear will laugh with me." The child grew, and was <u>weaned</u>; and Abraham made a great feast on the very day that Isaac was weaned, in gratitude to God for blessing them with this son of the covenant.

49

Abraham Offers Up Isaac

Genesis 22:1–19

WHEN Isaac became a young man, about twenty-five years old, God chose to test Abraham's faith in a most severe manner. God said to him, "Abraham"; and Abraham said, "Behold, here am I!" And God said, "Take now your son, your only son Isaac, whom you love so well, and go forth into the land of Moriah, and offer him there as a burnt offering upon one of the mountains of which I shall tell you."

being confused or puzzled — Abraham was deeply <u>perplexed</u> and troubled by this command of the Lord, but he was ready to trust God fully and to obey His will. So Abraham arose early the next morning, saddled his ass, and took his son Isaac with him, and also two of his young menservants. Abraham cut a bundle of wood to be used for the burnt offering and took it with him also. Then he set forth on the journey to the place of which God had told him.

Then, on the third day of the journey, Abraham lifted up his eyes and saw the place afar off. And Abraham said to his young men, "Wait here with the ass; I and the lad Isaac will go yonder and worship, and presently come back again to you."

over there

And Abraham took the bundle of wood for the burnt offering, and laid it on the back of Isaac his son to carry; and Abraham took in his own hand the fire and a knife. So Isaac went forth carrying on his back the wood for his own sacrifice. Thus the father and son went on together.

special gift or offering

Isaac said to Abraham his father, "My father"; and Abraham said, "Here am I, my son." Then Isaac said, "Behold the fire and the wood; but where is the lamb for a burnt offering?" Abraham replied, "My son, God will provide himself with a lamb for a burnt offering." So they journeyed on together.

When they came to the place on Mount Moriah of which God had told him, Abraham built an altar there, and laid the wood in order, and bound Isaac his son, and laid him on the altar upon the wood. And Abraham stretched forth his hand, and took the knife to slay his son. But the angel of the Lord called to him from heaven and said, "Abraham, Abraham"; and Abraham said, "Here am I." The angel said, "Do not lay your hand on the lad or harm him in any way; for now I know that you fear God, since you have not withheld your son, your only son, whom you love so well, from me."

And Abraham lifted up his eyes and looked, and behold, behind him was a ram, caught in a thicket by his horns. And Abraham went and took the ram, and offered it up as a burnt offering instead of his son. That is why Abraham called the name of that place Jehovah-jireh, which means "the Lord will provide." And in all the years following, the Hebrews continued to speak of that place, saying, "On the <u>mount</u> of the Lord it shall be provided." Over a thousand years later, Solomon built the temple of God upon Mount Moriah, the place where Abraham had offered up his son Isaac.

WORLD'S BIBLE STORY LIBRARY

mountain or hill

God commended Abraham for his faith and obedience, and reaffirmed the covenant that He had made with him at Hebron. For the angel of the Lord called to Abraham from heaven a second time and said, "The Lord says, 'By myself I have <u>sworn,</u> that because you have done this thing, and have not withheld your son, your only son, whom you love so well, I will bless you, and I will multiply your progeny as the stars of the heaven and as the sand which is on the seashore. And your descendants shall possess the gate of their enemies, and through your descendants shall all the nations of the earth be blessed, because you have obeyed my voice.'"

promised

So Abraham returned with Isaac to his young men, and they arose and went together to Beer-sheba; and Abraham dwelt at Beer-sheba.

Abraham took the knife to slay his son Isaac

Isaac Marries Rebekah

Genesis 24:1–67

THE years passed by and Isaac's mother Sarah died at the age of a hundred and twenty-seven years and was buried in the field of Machpelah, near Hebron in the land of Canaan. Abraham was also very old and was drawing near the end of his earthly journey. Before he died, he desired to see his son Isaac married to a woman of his own people.

So Abraham called his oldest and most trusted servant to him, and required an <u>oath</u> of him to the effect that he would help Isaac find a wife from his own people in Mesopotamia, and discourage him from taking a wife from the daughters of the Canaanites. Abraham also insisted that Isaac's wife should come back with him to live in the land which God had promised to Abraham and his descendants. So the old servant gave his solemn oath to Abraham that he would carry out his master's wishes in the matter.

Then the servant chose ten of Abraham's camels and departed, taking with him many gifts from his master. And he set forth on his journey and went to the city of Nahor in Mesopotamia. And he made the camels kneel down outside the city by a well of water at the time of evening when it was <u>customary</u> for the women to go out to draw water.

the usual thing to do

And the old servant prayed, "O Lord, God of my master Abraham, I pray you, give your servant good luck today, and show your loving-kindness to my master Abraham. Behold, I am standing here by the well of water, and the daughters of the men of the city are coming out to draw water. Let it happen that the maiden to whom I shall say, 'Let down your pitcher, I pray you, so that I may drink,' and who shall say, 'Drink, and I will let your camels drink also—let her be the one whom you have appointed for your servant Isaac. By this I shall know that you have shown your loving-kindness to my master."

Before the servant had finished praying, behold, Rebekah, the daughter of Bethuel, the son of Nahor, Abraham's brother, came out with her pitcher upon her shoulder. And she was a very beautiful young maiden. She went down to the well, and filled her pitcher, and came up again. The servant ran to meet her and said, "Let me, I pray you, drink a little water from your pitcher." With a smile Rebekah replied, "Drink, my lord"; and she promptly let down her pitcher upon her hand and gave him a drink. When she had finished

55

a drinking container
for animals

giving him a drink she said, "I will draw water for your camels too, until they have had enough to drink." And she promptly emptied her pitcher into the <u>trough</u> and ran again to the well to draw water, and she drew enough for all his camels. The old servant gazed at Rebekah without saying a word, anxious to discover whether the Lord had rendered his journey successful or not.

The servant then gave Rebekah a gold earring, and two gold bracelets for her wrists, and inquired about herself and her family. When he learned that she was a relative of Abraham's, he blessed God for leading him to his master's own people.

Then Rebekah ran and told her mother's household about these things. When Rebekah's brother Laban saw the expensive gifts his sister had received, he ran out to the man still waiting by the well and invited him to come and lodge in his house. Laban also ungirded the camels and prepared a place for them to rest and eat. When the servant came into the house, food was set before him, but he declined to eat until he had explained his errand.

Then he related to Rebekah's family the whole story of how his master Abraham had sent him to seek a wife for his son Isaac. He described how the Lord, in answer to his prayer, had led him to them through the kindness and help of Rebekah.

Abraham's servant asked Rebekah for a drink from her pitcher

Then Laban and Bethuel answered, "The thing comes from the Lord; we cannot speak to you bad or good. Behold, Rebekah is before you; take her and go, and let her be your master's son's wife, as the Lord has spoken."

When Abraham's servant heard their words, he bowed himself to the earth and worshiped the Lord. And he brought forth jewels of silver and jewels of gold, and clothing, and gave them to Rebekah. He also gave precious ornaments to her brother and to her mother. And he and the men who were with him ate and drank, and stayed the night.

honored and
praised God

When they arose in the morning, the servant said, "Send me back again to my master." But Rebekah's mother and brother said, "Let the maiden stay with us a few days longer, at least ten; after that she may go." But the servant said, "Do not make me wait, since the Lord has prospered my way; let me return at once to my master." Then they called Rebekah, and said to her, "Are you willing to go with this man?" She humbly replied, "I will go." So they sent away Rebekah their sister and her nurse, and Abraham's servant and his men. The servant prepared camels for Rebekah and her maidservants to ride on, and so they began the journey back to Abraham.

Meanwhile Isaac had come from the well Lahai-roi and was living in the south country. One evening Isaac went out in the field to meditate; and he lifted up his eyes and saw camels approaching. So he started out to meet whoever was coming. And Rebekah lifted up her eyes, and when she saw Isaac, she <u>alighted</u> from the camel, and said to the servant, "Who is that man coming across the field to meet us?" The servant said, "It is my master." Therefore Rebekah discreetly took her veil and covered her face.

And the servant told Isaac everything that he had done, in keeping with Abraham's request. Then Isaac brought Rebekah into his tent, and she became his wife; and he loved her. Thus Isaac was comforted after his mother's death. And God's covenant with Abraham was renewed through Isaac.

got down

How Jacob
Secured Esau's Birthright

Genesis 25:1–34

ABRAHAM was a hundred and seventy-five years old when he died and was gathered to his people. His sons Isaac and Ishmael buried him in the cave of Machpelah, where Sarah his wife was buried. After the death of Abraham God blessed his son Isaac. Isaac was dwelling by the well Lahai-roi.

Isaac was forty years old when he married Rebekah, the daughter of Bethuel the Syrian of Padan-aram. For twenty years after they were married, Isaac and Rebekah did not have any children to bless their home. This was a great disappointment to them, and Isaac prayed to the Lord and begged Him to send them a child.

The Lord heard Isaac's prayer, and in due time Rebekah found that she was going to have a child. In fact, Rebekah was to become the mother of twin boys.

Before her twin sons were born, Rebekah was quite ill and wondered whether she was going to live. She prayed to the Lord about her trouble, and the Lord said to her, "You shall give birth to two nations, and these shall be divided; the one people shall be stronger than the other, and the elder shall serve the younger."

When the time came, Rebekah gave birth to twin sons. Although the boys were twins, they were not at all alike. The first-born son, who was named Esau, was covered with soft red hair. He was called Esau because that name means "hairy." The twin brother was born right afterward; his little hand had taken hold of Esau's heel, so that he was called Jacob, which means "he seizes by the heel" or "he supplants." The father Isaac was sixty years old when his twin sons were born.

When Esau and Jacob grew up to be young men they were very unlike each other in appearance, character, and interests. Esau loved the out-of-doors. He roamed the fields and woods in search of wild animals and became a skillful hunter of all sorts of wild game. With his bow and arrows he killed many wild animals and brought the tasty meat home for his family to eat. His father Isaac was very fond of the tasty meat which Esau provided, and for this reason Esau was his favorite son.

Jacob was a quiet, thoughtful man who did not care for the kind of outdoor life that Esau loved. Jacob liked to stay at home and enjoy the shelter and comforts of their spacious tents. He was a home-loving youth and helped

takes place of, by force or plotting

enough stew for
a meal (vegetables
and meat)

certain favors given
to an oldest son

his mother with the tasks that had to be done each day. So Rebekah came to be very partial to her son Jacob.

Once when Esau was away on a hunting trip, Jacob stayed at home and boiled a <u>mess of pottage</u> made of lentils. Esau had been gone for some time, and when he came back from hunting he was faint with hunger. Smelling the savory pottage which Jacob was cooking, he exclaimed, "Give me, I pray you, some of your red pottage to eat, for I am faint with hunger!" When lentils are cooked they make a red pottage; so after this Esau was called Edom, which means "red."

Jacob had been waiting for an opportunity to take advantage of his brother Esau. The <u>birthright</u> belonged to Esau because he was the oldest son. This meant that he was entitled to a larger share of his father's possessions than Jacob. More important than that, it meant that the promises and blessings of the covenant which God had made with Abraham and Isaac would be passed on to the oldest son. Jacob wanted the birthright that belonged to Esau, and now he thought he had a good opportunity to take it from his unsuspecting brother.

So Jacob said to the famished Esau, "You must first sell me your birthright." Esau should have refused to consider it, but in his rough and carefree manner he replied, "I am on the point of death; what good will this

Jacob gave Esau food in exchange for his birthright

small flat seeds of pea
family used for food

birthright be to me?" Jacob wanted to make sure that Esau would not change his mind after he had satisfied his hunger, so he said, "Swear to me first that you will give me your birthright." So Esau took an oath and sold his birthright to Jacob. Then Jacob gave Esau bread and pottage of <u>lentils.</u> Esau ate and drank hungrily and greedily, and then rose up and went on his way again. Thus Esau despised his birthright, and surrendered it to his brother Jacob.

Jacob Obtains
Isaac's Blessing

Genesis 27:1–28:5

WHEN Isaac grew old and his eyes became dim so that he could not see, he called Esau his elder son, and said to him, "My son"; and Esau replied, "Here I am, father." Isaac said, "Behold, I am now old; I do not know the day of my death. Therefore, take your weapons, your quiver and your bow, and go out to the field and hunt for venison, and prepare for me the kind of savory meat that I love, and bring it to me so that I may eat of it, and bless you before I die."

Rebekah overheard what Isaac said to his son Esau. So when Esau went to the field to hunt for venison to bring to his father, Rebekah told her son Jacob what Isaac was planning to do. Then she said to Jacob, "My son, you must do what I command you. Go at once to the flock and bring me two good kids, and I will prepare from them the kind of savory meat for your father that he loves; and you shall take it to your father to eat, so that he may bless you before he dies."

Jacob said to Rebekah his mother, "Be-

savory *having a pleasing taste or smell*

WORLD'S
BIBLE STORY
LIBRARY

the asking of God's
favor

a spell of evil and
trouble

hold, Esau my brother is a hairy man and I am a smooth man. It may be that my father will feel me and discover that I am deceiving him; then I will bring a curse upon myself instead of a blessing." His mother replied, "Let your curse be upon me, my son; only do my bidding, and go, bring the kids to me." So Jacob went and brought them to his mother; and she prepared savory meat of the kind that his father loved.

Then Rebekah took from her elder son Esau the best garments which were in the house, and put them on Jacob her younger son. And she put the skins of the kids upon his hands and upon the smooth part of his neck. She then put the savory meat and the bread, which she had prepared, into the hand of her son Jacob.

So Jacob went to his father and said, "My father." Isaac said, "Here I am; who are you, my son?" Jacob said to his father, "I am Esau your first-born son. I have done as you bade me; now sit up, I pray you, and eat of my venison, so that you may bless me." But Isaac said to his son, "How is it that you have found it so quickly, my son?" Jacob replied, "Because the Lord your God has brought it to me." Then Isaac said to Jacob, "Come near, I pray you, so that I may feel you, my son, to learn whether you are really my son Esau or not."

So Jacob went near to Isaac his father, who

felt him and said, "The voice is Jacob's voice, but the hands are the hands of Esau." And he did not perceive that it was Jacob, because his hands were hairy like his brother Esau's hands; so he blessed him. Then Isaac said, "Are you really my son Esau?" Jacob replied, "I am." Then Isaac said, "Bring it to me and I will eat of your venison, so that I may bless you." So Jacob brought it to him, and he ate; and he brought him wine, and he drank. Then his father said to him, "Come near now and kiss me, my son." So Jacob came near and kissed him. And Isaac smelled his clothes, which were really Esau's, and bestowed his blessing upon Jacob, thinking that he was Esau.

As soon as Isaac had finished blessing Jacob, and when Jacob had scarcely gone out from the presence of his father, Esau his brother came in from his hunting. Esau had also prepared savory meat, and brought it now to his father. And Esau said to his father, "Let my father sit up, and eat of my venison, so that you may bless me." Isaac said to him, "Who are you?" Esau replied, "I am your son, your first-born son, Esau." Isaac trembled violently and said, "Who? Then who hunted for venison and brought it to me, and I ate of it before you came, and have blessed him? Yes, and he shall be blessed."

When Esau heard the words of his father, he cried out with an exceedingly great and bitter cry, and said to his father, "Bless me, even me also, O my father!" But Isaac said, "Your brother came with <u>craft,</u> and he has taken away your blessing." Esau said, "Is he not rightly named Jacob? For he has supplanted me these two times. He took away my birthright; and behold, now he has taken away my blessing. Have you not reserved a blessing for me?"

Isaac answered Esau, saying, "Behold, I have made Jacob your lord, and I have given him all his brothers for servants, and with grain and wine I have sustained him. What then shall I do for you, my son?" Esau said to his father, "Have you but one blessing, my father? Bless me, even me also, O my father." And Esau lifted up his voice and wept.

Now Esau hated Jacob for the way he had stolen his blessing, and Esau said to himself, "The days of <u>mourning</u> for my father are at hand; then I <u>will kill</u> my brother Jacob."

But these words of Esau her elder son were told to Rebekah. So she sent for Jacob her younger son and said to him, "Behold, your brother Esau consoles himself by preparing to kill you. Now therefore, my son, obey my voice; and arise, <u>flee</u> to Haran to Laban my brother, and stay with him for a while, until your brother's fury turns away from you and he forgets what you have done to him. Then I will send for you, and have you come back from Haran. Why should I lose both my sons

Isaac finished blessing Jacob

in one day?"

Then Rebekah planned how to get Isaac to approve sending Jacob away. She pretended that she feared Jacob would marry one of the Hittite women, instead of a woman of their own people.

So Isaac called Jacob and blessed him, and charged him not to marry one of the Canaanite women. Thus Isaac sent Jacob away; and he went to Padan-aram to Laban, the son of Bethuel the Syrian, the brother of Rebekah, Jacob's and Esau's mother.